REBELLION

Creative Director and CEO: Jason Kingsley
Chief Technical Officer: Chris Kingsley
Head of Books & Comics: Ben Smith
Roy of the Rovers Brand Manager: Rob Power
Roy of the Rovers Editor: Keith Richardson
Graphic Design: Sam Gretton

Published by Rebellion,
Riverside House, Osney Mead, Oxford, OX2 0ES, UK.
www.rebellionpublishing.co.uk

Manufactured in Ukraine by Imago.

First Printing: June 2019
10 9 8 7 6 5 4 3 2 1

www.royoftherovers.com

 royoftheroversofficial 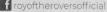 royoftheroversofficial royoftherovers

ROY OF THE ROVERS

GOING UP

ROB **WILLIAMS** BEN **WILLSHER**

BOOK THREE
GOING UP

Script
ROB WILLIAMS

Art
BEN WILLSHER

Letters
JIM CAMPBELL

Colours
JOHN CHARLES & **GUILHERME LINDEMBERG MENDES**

ROY RACE, JUST AFTER THE FIRST LEG OF THE PLAY-OFF SEMI-FINAL...

...EXTREMELY FRUSTRATED.

I DIDN'T DO IT!

...COURSE YOU DIDN'T, LOVE.

...YEAH...

...

IT LOOKED LIKE YOU DID IT.

WHY WOULD I HAND THE BALL OFF THE LINE IN THE LAST MINUTE AND GET SENT OFF, ROCKY?

DUH! TO STOP THEM SCORING AND BEATING YOU!

WHICH THEY DID! FROM THE PENALTY! SO YOU LOST AND NOW YOU'RE BANNED FROM THE SECOND LEG, YOU NUMPTY!

WE KNOW YOU'RE DISAPPOINTED ROY BUT TRY NOT TO BE SO HARD ON YOURSELF. IT'S... IT'S JUST AN INSTINCTIVE THING TO JUST...

INSTINCTIVE?

FFION... YOU...

YOU THINK I DID IT?

WE SAW THE TV REPLAY...

...

OH ROY.

ROY. BECKY GOFF, MELCHESTER LEADER. CAN I GET A QUICK QUOTE ABOUT YOUR RED CARD?

NO. I'M...

JUST SAY I'M GUTTED. THAT'S ALL.

IDIOT.

FFION, LOVE, HE'LL CALM DOWN. DO FORGIVE HIM.

HE'S DISAPPOINTED, IS ALL.

WE'RE ALL DISAPPOINTED, MRS RACE.

THERE'S STILL THE SECOND LEG, FFION.

NOT FOR ROY THERE'S NOT.

TWELVE TIMES. YOU GOT SENT OFF TWELVE TIMES. AND ONCE FOR ENGLAND.

...

ONCE OR TWICE, LIKE I SAID...

JOHNNY DEXTER, MELCHESTER'S FIRST-TEAM COACH.

I GOT SENT OFF ONCE OR TWICE. IT HAPPENS.

I KNOW HOW YOU'RE FEELING. YOU WANTED TO WIN SO BADLY. YOU WANTED TO HELP THE TEAM. BUT NOW YOU FEEL LIKE YOU'VE LET EVERYBODY DOWN.

AND YOU FEEL SICK AND GUILTY. IN YOUR GUT.

DON'T PUNISH YOURSELF, ROY RACE OF THE ROVERS. WITH THE ROCKET. WE'VE STILL GOT THE AWAY LEG. ONLY ONE GOAL DOWN. IT'S NOT OVER.

...

BUT I DIDN'T DO IT.

HONEST.

KEVIN 'MIGHTY' MOUSE. MELCHESTER'S MANAGER.

YOU'RE STARTING THE SECOND LEG, SON.

UP FRONT.

ME, GAFFER...?

I...

ARE YOU SURE I CAN...

PATRICK NOLAN. RESERVE STRIKER.

REALLY?

I HAVE *TOTAL* CONFIDENCE IN YOU, PATRICK. WE ALL DO.

YOU'RE A GOOD LITTLE PLAYER, SON. YOU JUST NEED TO BELIEVE IN YOURSELF.

AND MAYBE GROW TWO FEET IN HEIGHT...

NOT WRONG, PACO. KINGSBAY ARE GIANTS. THEY'LL EAT PATRICK ALIVE UNLESS HE FRONTS UP.

HE'LL BE ALRIGHT, BLACKIE. WE'LL GET HIM READY. WE'VE GOT A FEW DAYS.

HOPE YOU'RE RIGHT, ROY.

OR WE'RE IN TROUBLE.

72 HOURS BEFORE THE SECOND LEG OF THE PLAY-OFF SEMI.

FFION'S HOUSE.

AND VIC GUTHRIE'S.

OH... UH....

IS FFION IN?

...

I SAID IS...

I HEARD YOU, RACE. NOT DEAF, AM I?

WELL, IS SHE?

NO. OUT. SOMEWHERE. I DON'T LIKE THIS... YOU BEING 'FRIENDS' WITH MY SISTER, RACE.

I DON'T LIKE IT AT ALL.

AS MELCHESTER'S CAPTAIN I THINK I SHOULD BE ALLOWED TO, I DUNNO, *ORDER* YOU TO STOP DOING IT. OR SOMETHING.

VIC GUTHRIE. ROVERS' CAPTAIN. YEAH, I FORGOT THAT...

YOU'D **BEST** REMEMBER IT.

ALL ABOUT THE TEAM, *EH?* THAT'S A CAPTAIN. ITS LEADER, SOMEONE EVERYONE RESPECTS.

YOU GOT A POINT TO MAKE, RACE?

THE REF GOT IT WRONG. I DIDN'T SLAP THAT BALL OFF THE LINE, VIC.

I WONDER WHO DID?

AHHHHHHH!

SKIED IT!

I'M ALL FOR BEING SUPPORTIVE, GAFFER, BUT YOUNG PATRICK NEEDS BARN DOOR GLASSES ADJUSTMENT IF YOU ASK ME.

HIS MOVEMENT'S GREAT...HE'S SKILFUL. JUST NEEDS SOME CONFIDENCE.

CAN'T HIT A COW'S BACKSIDE WITH A TEASPOON AT THE MOMENT THOUGH, CAN HE? AND WE'VE GOT TO SCORE TWO AT KINGSBAY DUE TO AWAY GOALS, OR OUR SEASON'S OVER.

WE NEED GOALS.

THAT'S IT...I'VE HAD ENOUGH OF THIS.

ROY?

YOU OK?

NO.

THE REFEREE SENT OFF THE WRONG PLAYER. NO ONE WILL LISTEN TO ME.

SO MAYBE THE PRESS WILL...

DON'T.

Becky Goff
MELCHESTER LEADER

BLACKIE TOLD ME YOU WERE GOING TO TELL THE PRESS HOW YOU DIDN'T DO IT AND WERE GOING TO NAME THE PERSON THAT DID.

DON'T WHAT?

I KNOW HOW FRUSTRATED YOU ARE BUT IF YOU JUST DO THAT, YOU'LL JUST PULL THE WHOLE TEAM APART.

BUT...IF THEY LOOK AT THE FOOTAGE AGAIN I COULD GET CLEARED AND I *CAN* SCORE AGAINST KINGSBAY. I KNOW IT.

IF EVERYONE PLAYING FOR MELCHESTER ROVERS HATES ONE ANOTHER IT WON'T MAKE MUCH DIFFERENCE WHO'S UP FRONT.

...

YOU'RE RIGHT. SO I JUST HAVE TO TAKE IT? AND THE WHOLE SEASON'S FOR NOTHING.

NOT FOR NOTHING.

IT'S OK.

I'M SORRY I WAS OFF.

ZARAGOZA, COACH! IT IS NOT MY FAULT MY MOTHER MOVE TO MELCHESTER WITH THE RAIN, EH?

GOOD PLAYER THAT PACO DIAZ, EH? FAST!

BARRY 'MEAT' CLEAVER, MELCHESTER'S OWNER.

HMMM... YES, BARRY.

NOT THE FINISHED PRODUCT THOUGH. NOT YET. END PRODUCT NEEDS WORK.

NOT SOMETHING YOU'LL HAVE TO WORRY ABOUT, KEVIN.

BECAUSE I'VE JUST SOLD HIM! HE'S OFF IN THE SUMMER.

SLAP

WHAT?

TO TYNECASTER. THEY LIKED THE LOOK OF HIM IN THE FA CUP TIE AND HAVE BEEN KEEPING AN EYE ON HIM SINCE.

£350,000 WITH SOME *VERY* TASTY INCENTIVES DOWN THE ROAD IF HE TURNS OUT TO BE A PLAYER.

YES, LUV!

THERE IS *NOTHING* THE CLEAVER LIKES MORE THAN A SALE! *MEAT YOUR MASTER!*

SLAP

YOU CAN'T!

I...CAN'T?

I AM THE **OWNER** OF THIS FOOTBALL CLUB, KEVIN. THAT MEANS I AM YOUR **EMPLOYER.** WHICH MEANS I CAN DO WHATEVER I WANT!

WHICH INCLUDES SELLING OFF MEL PARK TO THE SUPERMARKETS FOR **MEGACASH** THE MOMENT YOUR TEAM DON'T GET PROMOTED!

MAGNIFICENT, IT'LL BE!

THE KING OF HYPERMARKETS! THE BIGGEST ONE IN ENGLAND! A **BARRYMARKET,** THEY'LL CALL IT!

GOT MY EYE ON THIS OLD WASTEDUMP LAND IN SCUDMORE. CHEAP AS CHIPS. SCUDMORE ROVERS! A NEW DAWN!

STILL, IF YOU DO PULL OFF A MIRACLE AND GO UP WE'LL GET THE CASH INFLUX FROM PROMOTION AND...OK...MAYBE I CAN SHELVE THE SALE FOR A YEAR.

I WAS THINKING, KEVIN, MIGHT BE BEST IF I GIVE THE TEAMTALK BEFORE THE SECOND LEG, *EH?* I'LL INSPIRE THE LADS A BIT MORE THAN YOU WILL.

I'VE GOT SOME THOUGHTS ON TEAM SELECTION I'D LIKE FOLLOWED TOO...

MY OFFICE. **NOW!**

EH? GET YOUR HANDS OFF...

NOW, BARRY!

FINE! BUT YOU FIRE ME *AFTER* THE SEASON ENDS OR I GO TO THE PRESS RIGHT NOW AND TELL THEM *EVERYTHING!*

YOU'RE FIRED, KEVIN MOUSE.

FIRED.

NO ONE TALKS TO BARRY LIKE THAT!

HOW DO YOU THINK THE PEOPLE OF MELCHESTER WILL REACT WHEN THEY FIND OUT THAT YOU'VE BEEN PLANNING TO SELL THEIR CLUB OFF TO A SUPERMARKET CHAIN THE LAST FEW MONTHS?

WHAT'LL THAT DO TO SALES OF CLEAVER MEAT PRODUCTS, EH?

ERM...

I'LL DO YOU A DEAL, BARRY. I'LL GO AND I'LL GO QUIETLY. *BUT...*

YOU WILL *NOT* SAY A WORD TO PACO, YOU WILL *NOT* SPEAK TO THE TEAM AND THEY WILL *NOT* HEAR A WORD ABOUT THE SALE OF THIS STADIUM, UNDERSTAND ME?

NOW LOOK HERE, KEVIN...

NOT. ONE. WORD. THESE LADS HAVE WORKED *SO HARD* TO HAVE A CHANCE OF PROMOTION. NO ONE GAVE THEM A CHANCE. THE FANS ARE COMING BACK.

THEY DESERVE TO BE ABLE TO *HOPE...*

OK, KEVIN. DEAL. BUT THE MOMENT YOU LOSE...

YOU ARE *SACKED,* SON!

WE WON'T LOSE THEN! WE'LL GET PROMOTED, BARRY!

YOU WAIT AND SEE!

SLAM

...

WE'LL WIN ON SATURDAY.

...WE HAVE TO.

...

EVERYTHING ALRIGHT, MOUSE?

FINE, JOHNNY.

LET'S WORK ON ATTACKING CORNERS, SHALL WE?

24 HOURS BEFORE THE GAME.

YOU'RE HAVING A LAUGH...

...

SAY THAT AGAIN!

BLAH BLAH...AFTER FURTHER EVIDENCE HAS COME TO LIGHT AND BEEN EXAMINED FULLY BY THE DISCIPLINARY BOARD... BLAH *VERY* BORING BLAH...

"ROY RACE'S RED CARD HAS BEEN **RESCINDED**." WHICH, IN ENGLISH, MEANS 'WE WERE STUPID AND WRONG AND STUPID'.

WHICH MEANS ROY IS FREE TO PLAY AGAINST KINGSBAY.

YES!

HA! YOU'VE GOT A GUARDIAN ANGEL, MATE.

FATE, ROY! BOUND TO SCORE NOW, EH? *HAVE* TO!

BUT, WHY DID THEY CHANGE THEIR MINDS?

BECAUSE VIC HERE WROTE TO THEM AND TOLD THEM THAT *HE* HANDLED THE BALL.

...WHAT?

WE'VE JUST BEEN TO LONDON TO SEE THE BOARD IN PERSON. VIC'S NOW GOT THE BAN INSTEAD.

WHAT?

WHY?

BECAUSE I'M MELCHESTER'S CAPTAIN.

ALL ABOUT THE TEAM, EH?

AND WELCOME TO BAY HILL, HOME TO KINGSBAY, WHO HOST THIS SECOND LEG OF THE DIVISION 2 PLAYOFFS SEMI-FINAL.

KINGSBAY COME INTO THE GAME EXTREMELY CONFIDENT OF PROGRESSING TO THE PLAYOFF FINAL HAVING WON THE AWAY LEG 2-1.

IT'S DIFFICULT TO SEE HOW THE YOUNGSTERS OF MELCHESTER CAN COPE WITH KINGSBAY'S PHYSICAL PRESENCE.

GONNA CRUSH YER...

BAILEY 9

BZZZZZ

Good luck, my friend. I will be watching.

WHO...IS... THIS?

TAP TAP TAP TAP

Good luck, my friend. I will be watching.

who is this?

Hugo.

BZZZZZ

SICK...

AND WE'RE UNDERWAY HERE AT KINGSBAY. THE PLAYOFF FINAL AWAITS THE WINNER AND A CHANCE TO WIN PROMOTION TO **DIVISION ONE!**

YOU SURE YOU DON'T WANT ROY AND BLACKIE UP TOP TOGETHER? WE'VE GOT TO SCORE TWO HERE.

FOR THE LOSER, THE SEASON ENDS HERE

NO, BLACKIE DROPPING INTO MIDFIELD. STAY SOLID EARLY. BE PATIENT.

SECOND MINUTE HERE AND THE KINGSBAY MIDFIELDER McMAHON IS RUNNING RIGHT AT MELCHESTER'S MIDFIELD.

THEY'RE TAKING THE DIRECT ROUTE, EARLY.

SOMEONE **TACKLE** HIM!

CENTRE OF MIDFIELD...

EXACTLY WHERE I'D BE...

BRAVE SAVE BY GORDON STEWART, MELCHESTER'S SCOTTISH GOALIE.

BUT HE'S TAKEN A HEAVY KNOCK THERE.

YOU OK, GORDON?

YEAH... I...

=SPIT=

I'M ALRIGHT. CAUGHT ME ON THE CHIN IS ALL. I'M GOOD.

UNINTENTIONAL THAT, BOYS. HE WAS REACHING FOR THE BALL. BUT I'M GIVING A YELLOW FOR THE CONTACT.

AND THAT'S THE FIRST YELLOW OF THE SEMI, FOR KINGSBAY STRIKER COLE.

BoOOOOOOOOOOOOOOlooo!!!

DON'T KNOW ABOUT YOU, PACO...

BUT I'VE HAD ENOUGH OF THIS.

SÍ.

AND NOW MELCHESTER ARE STARTING TO LOSE THEIR HEADS. THAT'S A FOUL BY RACE...

NO, HE GOT THE BALL! THE REFEREE IS WAVING PLAY ON...

PACO DIAZ ON THE RUN... **OH!** GREAT DRIBBLE.

DIAZ **SQUARES** IT TO GRAY...

PENALTY! OH! HAS TO BE!

HE TOOK THE BALL FIRST. CORNER KICK!

YOU ARE **JOKING**, REF!

HE NEAR BROKE HIS ANKLE.

CORNER. KICK.

YOU GOING TO BE ABLE TO CARRY ON, BLACKIE?

I...YEAH... I'LL BE OK.

I'LL BE THE JUDGE OF THAT.

DIAZ TAKES THE CORNER FOR MELCHESTER.

RACE FLICKS IT ON....LOFTY PEAK MEETS IT!

BULLET HEADER! AND ROVERS ARE LEVEL ON THE NIGHT! IT'S 1-1 HERE!

BUT KINGSBAY STILL LEAD 3-2 ON AGGREGATE.

COME ON... ONE MORE AND WE'RE LEVEL ON AGGREGATE.

COME ON!

HA. THE CENTRE HALF...WITH THE HEAD! YES! THAT CORNER MOVE WORKED PERFECTLY, MOUSE! WE ARE GENIUSES! YES!

GONE QUIET NOW, HAVEN'T THEY, THE CROWD?.

JUST BEFORE HALF-TIME. HOW'S BLACKIE?

NOT GOOD. I'M NOT SURE HE CAN PLAY ON.

I CAN PLAY ON! I'M PLAYING ON!

SHUSH YOU.

AND IT'S HALF-TIME HERE!

NOT SO COCKY NOW ARE THEY, VERNON?

NO ROY, THEY ARE NOT. ONE MIGHT EVEN SAY THEY LOOK A BIT... WORRIED?

SHADDUP YOU TWO.

RIGHT! TIME FOR THE CLEAVER TO INSPIRE THEM, I THINK.

OUT OF THE WAY KEVIN! I WILL GIVE THE TEAMTALK HERE!

NO BARRY. YOU WILL NOT.

THIS IS MY CHANGING ROOM. MAYBE FOR THE LAST TIME.

BUT IT IS MINE.

ENJOY YOUR LAST EVER TEAMTALK, KEVIN.

WHATEVER HAPPENS IN THIS SECOND HALF YOU ARE FINISHED HERE.

I'M NOT WAITING! I'VE GOT SOMEONE ALREADY LINED UP, LAD. GOING TO ANNOUNCE HIM NEXT WEEK.

YOUR DAYS AT MELCHESTER ARE DONE.

... WIN, LADS.

YOU'RE BETTER THAN THEM.

YOU PLAY FOOTBALL THE RIGHT WAY. PASS, MOVE, PACE. SPEED-OF-THOUGHT.

YOU'RE YOUNG. YOU'RE THE FUTURE. THEY ARE THE PAST. THEIR WAY...

YOU ARE MELCHESTER ROVERS.

AND YOU ARE GOING TO DO SUCH GREAT THINGS.

WIN.

HHHNNHHH...

TEN MINUTES INTO THE SECOND HALF HERE AND MOMENTUM HAS SHIFTED. BLACKIE GRAY POKES IT THROUGH TO **RACE!**

HE'S IN ON GOAL!

IT'S IN!

RACE HAS SCORED! WE'RE LEVEL ON AGGREGATE HERE! 3-3!

GET INNNNNNNN!

YESSSSSOSSSSSS!

AND ROVERS ARE RAMPANT. VERNON ELLIOT NOW--**ELECTRIC PACE!** OH, HE'S GONE PAST THE KINGSBAY RIGHT BACK ON THE OUTSIDE.

KINGSBAY-- WHETHER IT'S THE PRESSURE OR SIMPLY THE YOUNG LEGS OF MELCHESTER--ARE BEING LEFT LIKE STATUES HERE.

ELLIOT SQUARES IT... **HARD!**

RIGHT, MOUSE!

NOW YOU ARE FIRED. HA! CLEAR YOUR THINGS AND GET OUT! WADDYA THINK OF...

...

KEVIN?

WHY ARE YOU ON THE FLOOR?

...WE WON, BARRY.

...

THE BOYS WON.

THE NATIONAL STADIUM...THE PLAYOFFS FINAL. CAN YOU BELIEVE IT?

NO.

YEAH... NO...NO, I CAN'T...

YOU RECKON CLEAVER WILL BUY US SUITS...?

WOOOAHHHAWOOOAHHHH

HAVE YOU SEEN HIM, JOHNNY?

IS MIGHTY MOUSE OK?

ARE YOU THE MANAGER NOW?

... KEVIN MOUSE IS YOUR MANAGER, LAD.

OUR MANAGER.

I DIDN'T...

I DIDN'T MEAN...IT'S JUST... WE'VE GOT THE PLAYOFFS FINAL IN A WEEK AND...

IT'S OK, GORDON. WE KNOW. JOHNNY'LL BE THE CARETAKER UNTIL...

NO, HE WON'T.

THIS IS A BIG GAME, LADS. A *HUGE* GAME!

AND YOU LADS DESERVE A *HUGE* MANAGER.

AND THAT IS *EXACTLY* WHAT BARRY CLEAVER HAS DELIVERED.

THE WAY HE ALSO DELIVERS THE *FINEST MEAT CUTS* TO YOUR SUPERMARKET!

BARRY! BARRY! THIS IS A **REAL** SCOOP FOR MELCHESTER, A CLUB WITH NO MONEY.

HOW HAVE YOU MANAGED TO BRING HOT-SHOT BACK FROM THE SOUTH OF SPAIN, WHERE HE'S BEEN LIVING THESE PAST TEN YEARS?

I'LL ANSWER THAT IF I MAY, BARRY.

MELCHESTER HAS ALWAYS BEEN IN MY HEART AND BARRY HERE IS A VERY GOOD, CLOSE PERSONAL FRIEND OF MINE, YE KEN? HE TOLD ME THE CLUB NEEDED ME AND, WELL...

I **HAD** TO COME BACK.

BUT HOT-SHOT, YOU ONLY PLAYED FOR ROVERS FOR ONE SEASON BEFORE LEAVING FOR WHAT WAS THEN A RECORD SUM TO SPAIN.

AND NOW I'M BACK, TO SPRINKLE A LITTLE SCOTTISH STARDUST ON MEL PARK ONCE MORE, EH?

WELL, ON THE NATIONAL STADIUM, ACTUALLY, FOR THE PLAY-OFF FINAL. BUT YOU CANNY LADS KNOW WHAT I MEAN, EH? HA!

HAMISH HERE WILL MANAGE MELCHESTER ROVERS...

DON'T YOU MEAN CARETAKER-MANAGE? KEVIN MOUSE IS STILL YOUR MANAGER, ISN'T HE?

YES. OF COURSE. HAMISH WILL BE **CARETAKER** MANAGER. AND AS WE ALL KNOW, HE HAS EXPERIENCE OF MANAGEMENT AT THE TOP LEVEL IN SPAIN...

LASTED FIVE GAMES AT REAL BEFORE BEING SACKED. FOR BEING TACTICALLY CLUELESS. LOST FOUR. DREW ONE. AND THEY CONCEDED FIVE HIS LAST GAME.

YOU'RE NOT A FAN THEN?

I AM NOT, ROY RACE, OF THE ROVERS WITH THE ROCKET, NO.

I PLAYED WITH HAMISH AT ROVERS. HE WAS BRILLIANT BUT HE KNEW IT. NEVER LISTENED TO ANYONE. HE LEFT FOR THE MONEY AND THE FAME AND THAT'S WHAT HE'S **ALWAYS** BEEN ABOUT.

ONLY OUT FOR HIMSELF. AND THE MOMENT HE WENT, THE WHOLE CLUB...EVERYONE JUST WANTED THE CASH. OTHERS FOLLOWED... BUT HE STARTED THE ROT.

AND BESIDES...

"IF HE'S A FRIEND OF CLEAVER'S I DON'T TRUST HIM."

HAMISH! HAMISH! WHAT ABOUT RUMOURS OF YOU BEING BANKRUPT AND THE SPANISH COURTS WANTING TO TALK TO YOU ABOUT UNPAID TAX?

IS THAT WHY YOU'RE BACK?

THANK YOU LADS AND LADIES! THANK YOU! NO FURTHER QUESTIONS!

HOLD ON A MINUTE, BARRY.

I WANT TO SAY SOMETHING.

HOW **DARE** YOU...

...I WAS A **WORLD-CLASS** FOOTBALLER, YOU KNOW. WORLD. CLASS.

COME ON, HAMISH! FOR GOODNESS SAKE.

TWENTY-FIVE GOALS FOR SCOTLAND! TWENTY OF THEM ABSOLUTE BELTERS! HOW MANY DID YOU SCORE FOR SCOTLAND, EH PAL?

HE'S...

...WHAT'S HAPPENING? IS HE...

IS HE CRYING?

I AM HOT-SHOT HAMISH, YOU KNOW!

HOT. SHOT. HAMISH.

DO YOU REMEMBER THAT GOAL I SCORED FOR SCOTLAND AGAINST BRAZIL IN THE WORLD CUP, LADDIE? OCH, THAT WAS A *RIGHT* BELTER.

THAT... THAT'S OUR NEW MANAGER.

HE'S A BIT.... ERRATIC.

FIVE DAYS BEFORE THE PLAY-OFF FINAL.

HOW'S THE ANKLE, BLACKIE? YOU GOING TO BE ABLE TO PLAY?

YES.

WE'LL SEE...

FOUR DAYS BEFORE THE PLAY-OFF FINAL.

WHAT HAPPENS IF BLACKIE CAN'T GO?

YOU UP TOP ON YOUR OWN. PATRICK'S NERVES ARE TERRIBLE AND A MAJOR FINAL? HE WON'T COPE. BUT, AT LEAST WE'LL HAVE VIC BACK.

OUR MANAGER HAVE AN OPINION ON THAT?

NO IDEA, SON.

NONE.

TWO DAYS BEFORE THE PLAY-OFF FINAL.

...IS HE OK?

YEAH. THEY THINK.

THEY'VE OPERATED AND PUT IN SOMETHING CALLED A 'STENT'. I DON'T UNDERSTAND IT. BUT THE DOCTORS SAY HE SHOULD BE GOOD.

HAS HIS FAMILY COME TO VISIT?

I DON'T KNOW IF HE HAS ANY. HIS LIFE WAS THE CLUB. *IS* THE CLUB.

I'M GOING TO GET BACK TO MEL PARK. TRAINING. MAKE SURE HAMISH HASN'T, I DUNNO, DECIDED TO NOT PLAY A GOALIE ON SATURDAY OR SOMETHING.

JOHNNY?

JUST SIT WITH HIM, YOU TWO.

UH...

HE'S ON PAIN MEDICATION. BUT I SUPPOSE HE CAN HEAR US. TELL HIM ABOUT THE TEAM.

...OK.

ALRIGHT, GAFFER? THE BOYS ALL SAY HI. TRAINING'S GOING WELL. JOHNNY HAS US DOING NON-STOP DRILLS. YOU KNOW HOW IT IS?

...UM.

PACO'S FREEKICKS ARE GETTING EVEN MORE DEADLY. HE'S BEEN PRACTICING.

...PACO.

CLEAVER...
GOING TO SELL
PACO TO TYNECASTER.
GOING TO SELL
MEL PARK.

GOT TO
WIN.

GOT TO GET
PROMOTED.

I THINK
HE NEEDS
HIS REST,
LUVS.

DO YOU
THINK IT'S
TRUE?

AND THAT'S
WHY MOUSE HAD
THE HEART
ATTACK?

THAT...
MAKES SENSE.
BUT...IF IT IS.
WHAT DO
WE DO?

GIVE ME
YOUR
PHONE!

WHY?

BARRY
CLEAVER
DESERVES A
SHOCK.

BECKY GOFF
MELCHESTER
LEADER

CALL

THE MELCHESTER LEADER

CLEAVER PLANS TO SELL ROVERS TO SUPERMARKET CHAIN!

WAS GOING TO SACK MOUSE!

WHAT?

WHAT?

WHAT... WHAT'S THAT NOISE?

IT'S GETTING BIGGER?

WHAT IS?

THE CROWD.

THE PLAY-OFF FINAL!

THIS IS IT! THE NATIONAL STADIUM!

THE HOME OF FOOTBALL IN THE COUNTRY THAT INVENTED THE SPORT!

AND THERE ARE 50,000 FANS EXPECTED TODAY!

PRETTY MUCH THE WHOLE OF COURT PARK AND MELCHESTER HAVE MADE IT DOWN THE M5 TO LONDON TODAY!

MELCHESTER ROVERS
14 ROY RACE

WELL, THE HALF OF MELCHESTER THAT DON'T SUPPORT TYNECASTER, OF COURSE.

HAHAHA.

AND IF YOU ARE A MELCHESTER FAN YOU'RE OUT FOR BLOOD, ESPECIALLY FROM YOUR CHAIRMAN, BARRY 'MEAT' CLEAVER.

THERE IS **NO** SUBSTANCE TO THOSE STORIES, I PROMISE YOU. **FAKE NEWS!**

KEVIN MOUSE WILL BE OUR MANAGER AGAIN WHEN HE RECOVERS. YOU HAVE MY WORD. AND MY WORD IS MY **MEAT**, AS I SAY.

ROVERS! ROVERS! COURT PARK! COURT PARK!

THEY WANT TO SELL OUR STADIUM. CHANGE OUR NAME. WANT TO GET RID OF OUR MANAGER.

WE DON'T LET THEM.

THE TOTA

AND WE'RE UNDERWAY HERE FOR THE **DIVISION 2 PLAY-OFF FINAL.**

Gola REBELLION Gola REBELLION

COURT PARK, WHO SO NEARLY ACHIEVED AUTOMATIC PROMOTION--JUST MISSING OUT ON GOAL DIFFERENCE-- VERSES MELCHESTER ROVERS.

MELCHESTER ENJOYED A LATE RUN TO THE PLAY-OFF PLACES PLAYING SOME SPARKLING FOOTBALL. BUT IS TODAY TOO SOON FOR THEIR YOUNGSTERS?

EARLY SKIRMISHES HERE. VIC GUTHRIE, ROVERS' CAPTAIN, BACK AFTER SUSPENSION, HEADS IT ON.

AND IT'S IN!
IT'S IN!

MELCHESTER LEAD HERE. IT'S 1-0 TO THE ROVERS!

ALRIGHT, HAMISH. WHAT SHOULD WE DO NOW?

DO YOU WANT US TO SIT BACK, DEFEND? ATTACK? WHAT?

...

I DINNAE KNOW.

TRUTH BE TOLD, JOHNNY. I WAS AN AWESOME PLAYER. BUT I'M NO MUCH OF A MANAGER. I THINK WE BOTH KNOW THAT.

BUT I DO WANT THE BOYS TO **WIN.**

SO WHY DON'T... YERKNOW...YOU TELL THEM WHIT TO DAE.

BUT CLEAVER...?

OCH MAN, CLEAVER'S A BIG HEIDTHABA'. WE BOTH KNOW THAT.

A WHAT?

GAWAN, JOHNNY. TELL THEM WHIT TO DAE! WHILE I SIT HERE AND INSPIRE THEM BY...Y'KNOW, LOOKING **AMAZING.**

DUNCAN! ASIF! STAY BACK! DON'T GET CAUGHT!

GUTHRIE! GUTHRIE! SIT! SIT!

THAT'S IT, DEXTER. MANAGER AND ASSISTANT MANAGER EXACTLY AS THEY **SHOULD** BE.

OOF.

ROVERS, WITH JUST ONE UP FRONT, ARE FINDING IT DIFFICULT TO MAKE THE BALL STICK.

AND YOU CAN SEE WHAT A TIDY FOOTBALLING OUTFIT COURT PARK ARE...

JENKINS LOOKS TO THE FAR POST.

THAT'S A TANTALISING CROSS!

IT'S THE EQUALIZER! MORRISON COULDN'T MISS!

1-1 HERE! AND ALL THE MOMENTUM IS WITH COURT PARK WITH HALF-TIME APPROACHING.

YOU LOOK EXHAUSTED.

I DON'T THINK I REALISED HOW MUCH OF THE DONKEY WORK BLACKIE WAS DOING FOR ME. YOU GET BATTERED AS A LONE STRIKER.

HALF-TIME!

ATTACK THEM! THAT'S WHIT I SAE LADS! CHUCK ON ANOTHER STRIKER OR TWO AND *GO FIR THEM!*

DEATH OR GLORY, EH?

BZZZZZz

MIGHTY MOUSE

Stick Patrick on for heaven's sake!

AMAZINGLY, HAMISH, I AGREE WITH YOU.

AND SO DOES MIGHTY MOUSE, LADS.

AY?

PATRICK. YOU'RE ON, SON.

COURT PARK!

WOW.

COURT PARK!

MELCHESTER! MELCHESTER!

AND THE SECOND HALF'S UNDERWAY HERE BUT THE DIRECTION OF THIS GAME HASN'T CHANGED.

COURT PARK ARE RAMPANT HERE.

NAVID IS IN ON GOALLLLL...

OH! BRILLIANT SAVE BY GORDON STEWART!

FIVE MINUTES LEFT.

WHAT ARE YOU **DOING**, MAN?

I CANNAE LOOK!

YOU'RE OUR MANAGER! OUR CARETAKER MANAGER BUT OUR MANAGER NONETHE...

OH NO. THEY'RE IN AGAIN.

AND NAVID HAS CAUGHT THE ROVERS ON THE BREAK AGAIN.

GO ON, COURT PARK...

MAKE BARRY A MINT.

WHAT A BLOCK BY LOFTY PEAK!

A DEFINITE GOAL SAVED.

PATRICK NOLAN IS THEEEEEEERRE!!

ROVERS HAVE WON IT! SURELY!

MELCHESTER... INCREDIBLE!

PATRICKKKKKK!!

AFTER ALL THEY'VE BEEN THROUGH THIS SEASON... MELCHESTER ROVERS ARE GOING TO BE PROMOTED TO LEAGUE ONE!

"ALL ABOUT THE TEAM, EH?"

...YEAH...

BRILLIANT.

AFTERWARDS.

YOU DID IT!

WE DID IT. ALL OF US.

NEVER IN DOUBT, WAS IT?

...

ALRIGHT, VIC.

I'M NOT LOOKING AT THIS, RACE. AT ALL.

ROY RACE.

HUGO...

I ASK AGAIN, ARE YOU *SURE* YOU ARE NOT BRAZILLIAN MY FRIEND? BECAUSE THAT STEPOVER AT THE END? IT WAS *PURE* SAO PAOLO...

UHHH...NO. MELCHESTER. DEFINITELY...MELCHESTER. HUGO, THIS IS FFION GUTHRIE. SHE...

I PLAY CENTRE MIDFIELD FOR SOWERBY WOMEN'S TEAM.

I REMEMBER.

IT IS GOOD TO SEE YOU AGAIN, FFION. ROY, I HAVE SOMEONE I WOULD LIKE TO INTRODUCE YOU TO ALSO...

END OF BOOK THREE
SEE YOU NEXT SEASON!

ROY OF THE ROVERS.
THE FIRST SEASON

Keep track of every new *Roy of the Rovers* book here!
Don't forget to tick the boxes as you read each one.

FICTION

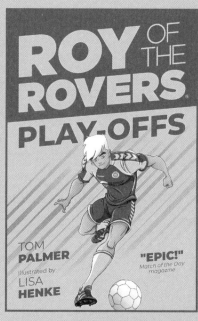

BOOK 1
SCOUTED

Author: Tom Palmer
Out: October 2018
ISBN: 978-1-78108-698-8

Roy Race is the most
talented striker in Melchester
– but is he good enough
to catch the eye of the
Melchester Rovers scouts?

READ? ☐

BOOK 2
TEAMWORK

Author: Tom Palmer
Out: February 2019
ISBN: 978-1-78108-707-7

Life gets tricky for Roy as
he adjusts to life in the
spotlight. Fortune and glory
await, but can Roy juggle
football, fame and family?

READ? ☐

BOOK 3
PLAY-OFFS

Author: Tom Palmer
Out: May 2019
ISBN: 978-1-78108-722-0

Crunch time for Rovers: the end
of the season is here, the club is
in deep trouble, and it's down
to Roy to bring a bit of hope
back to the Melchester faithful.

READ? ☐

GRAPHIC NOVELS

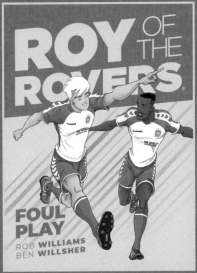

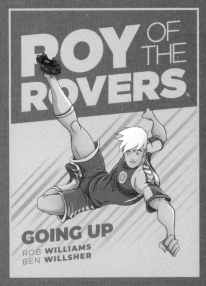

BOOK 1
KICK-OFF

Writer: Rob Williams
Artist: Ben Willsher
Out: November 2018
ISBN: 978-1-78108-652-0

Roy Race is 16, talented, and desperate to make it as a footballer. But is he good enough for Melchester Rovers? Now's the time to prove if he's got what it takes to become Roy of the Rovers.

READ? ☐

BOOK 2
FOUL PLAY

Writer: Rob Williams
Artist: Ben Willsher
Out: March 2019
ISBN: 978-1-78108-669-8

Roy picks up an injury that puts him on the sidelines, and suddenly there's competition for his place as a brand new - and brilliant - striker is brought in by the management...

READ? ☐

BOOK 3
GOING UP

Writer: Rob Williams
Artist: Ben Willsher
Out: June 2019
ISBN: 978-1-78108-673-5

Roy and the team have battled through a tough season, but have they got enough left to get promoted? Or will they fall at the final hurdle and see the club sold by its greedy owner?

READ? ☐

PLAYER
INTERVIEW

Introduce yourself

Patrick Nolan – striker.

Do you have a nickname?

Not really...the lads call me Pat or Patty.

Who was your favourite team growing up?

Ballybunion Wanderers. They were the first
Irish league team that I played for. At one
stage I was a lot more into playing hurling,
but then the Wanderers came calling and I
never looked back.

**Who is the best player that you have
played with?**

Roy and Paco are both fantastic. Those boys
are a different level, like. Hopefully, I can learn
enough from them both, especially Roy.
Who needs Hugo when you have the Racey!

**Who is the best player that you have
played against?**

Wow – that's a hard one! I can't think of his
name right now, but one of the Kingsbay
centre-backs is tough to play against. He's
not necessarily the most skillful player, but
he's built like a barn and very intimidating!

Do you have a pre-match routine?

I try and hide from Vic. He does this thing
where he comes up to you and screams in
your face...it's weird man!

What's your advice to young players?

Don't be afraid to learn what you can from
the players around you.

**What's your favourite social media
network and why?**

I'm not much of a techy fella - Facebook is
the only thing that I go on regularly.

PLAYER
INTERVIEW

Introduce yourself

Vic Guthrie – midfielder and captain for Melchester Rovers

Do you have a nickname?

Captain Fantastic! The welsh Wizard! Okay, so the players don't call me either of these names, but I wouldn't discourage them if they did!

Who was your favourite team growing up?

My grandfather played for Neath United, so I was very fond of them. One of my earliest memories is of Melchester playing Weston Villa in the cup final. After that I was Melchester Rovers all the way!

Who is the best player that you have played with?

As captain, I shouldn't really say. Ask me again in twenty years when I've retired! I'll give you the answer from my super-deluxe villa in the Bahamas!

Who is the best player that you have played against?

I don't look at individual players in that way. The opposition are the opposition – the eleven men facing you on the pitch. The best team that I've played against so far is Tynecaster.

Do you have a pre-match routine?

I control the music in the dressing room. It's always something loud to get the lads in the mood. Then I go around to each player and get right up in their face and scream! Gets their blood pumping. It's the same ritual Johnny Dexter used to have back in his playing days.

What's your advice to young players?

Give nothing less than 100% every time you get onto the pitch. If you have the talent and you do that, you'll make it. If not, get out of the way!

What's your favourite social media network and why?

Tumblr. I have a lot of my greatest tackles edited together on my blog.